DAX'S COMET

First published in Great Britain in 1995 by Boxtree Limited, Broadwall House, 21 Broadwall, London SE1 9PL. Published under exclusive license from Paramount Pictures, the trademark
STAR TREK: DEEP SPACE NINE art and text material © 1994 Paramount Pictures. All rights reserved. STAR TREK is a registered trademark of Paramount Pictures. STAR TREK: DEEP
NINE is ™ ® © 1994 Paramount Pictures. All rights reserved. Any similarity to persons living or dead is purely coincidental. With the exception of artwork used for review purposes, none
Kilbride. A CIP catalogue entry for this book is available from the British Library.

STAR TREK®
DEEP SPACE NINE™

DAX'S COMET

BOXTREE

Jerry Bingham
Charles Marshall
writers

Tim Eldred
Leonard Kirk
pencillers

Bruce McCorkindale
inker

Tim Eldred
Patrick Owsley
letterers

Moose Baumann
Barry Gregory
color design

Violent Hues
'Bu Tones
color separations

Mark Paniccia
editor

MEANWHILE...

NOW, SUPPOSE YOU FILL US IN ON WHAT'S *WRONG* WITH OUR SECURITY CHIEF?

FROM WHAT I SAW DURING MY BRIEF TIME WITH HIM, HE SEEMED HIGHLY *AGITATED*...

...EXTREMELY *PARANOID* AND CONSIDERABLY *DANGEROUS*.

DANGEROUS? THAT DOESN'T SOUND LIKE ODO, DOCTOR.

I DON'T BELIEVE IT *IS* ODO.

I SUSPECT HE'S SUFFERING FROM SOME UNKNOWN *SIDE EFFECT* OF THE VACCINATION SHOT.

IF *THAT'S* THE CASE, THEN THIS HAS GONE FROM A *TEST RUN*...

...TO THE *REAL THING*.

SOON AFTER, IN A FAR CORNER OF THE STATION...

...SO COLD... NEVER BEEN SO COLD...

I'M HERE, ODO. I'M HERE FOR YOU.

NO... WON'T LET YOU...TAKE ME.

LOOK AT ME, ODO. I'VE KNOWN YOU LONGER THAN ANYONE HERE.

I CAN HELP YOU GET THROUGH THIS, BUT ONLY IF YOU TRUST ME.

YOU'RE WITH FRIENDS HERE, ODO.

ALL WE WANT TO DO IS HELP YOU.

...I DON'T KNOW...

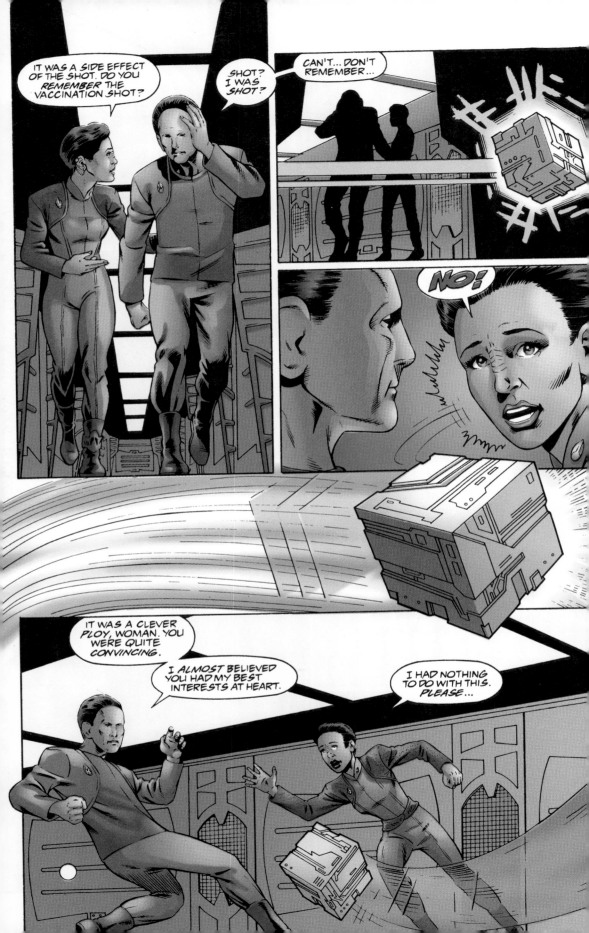

BASHIR TO COMMANDER SISKO...

I'VE FOUND HIM.

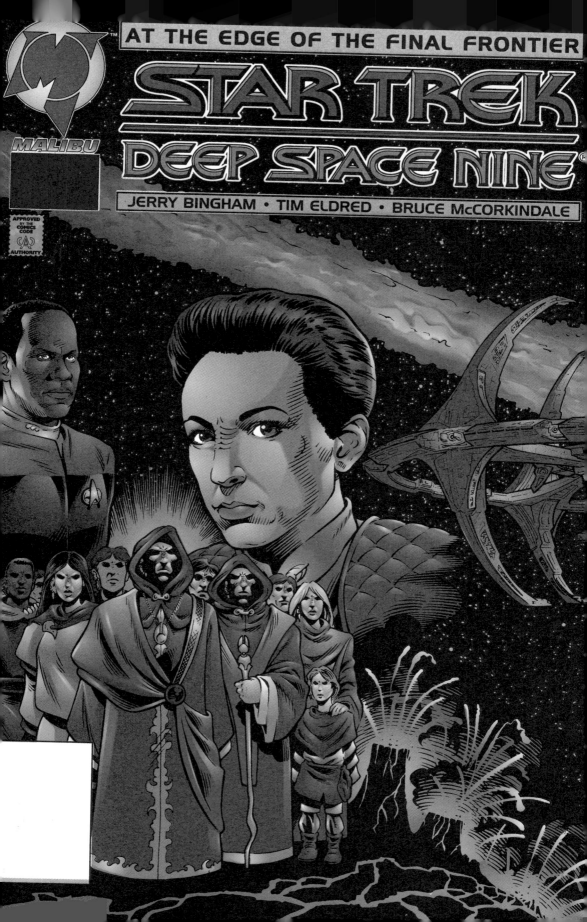

DO WE *KILL* THEM, EMINENCE?

THEY *CAN'T* BE ALLOWED TO RETURN TO THE SURFACE! *NOT NOW!*

DO WE ALLOW THEM TO *LIVE* WITH US? WE HAVE *STRICT* POPULATION CONTROL LAWS!

BESIDES, THEY WOULD ONLY TRY TO ESCAPE BACK TO THE SURFACE.

THE BAJORANS HAVE ALWAYS KNOWN OF YOUR EXISTENCE...

YOU SPEAK AS IF WE ARE NOT *BAJORANS.* UPLANDER, WE WERE THE *FIRST*--

ENOUGH!!

YOU UPLANDERS MIGHT HAVE *SUSPECTED*, BUT YOU KNOW *NOTHING* OF OUR EXISTENCE HERE.

OUR *EMISSARIES* HAVE WALKED AMONG YOU FOR *CENTURIES*... YET YOU KNOW OF US ONLY AS A *MYTHOLOGICAL* SOCIETY... INHABITING STORIES YOU USE TO FRIGHTEN CHILDREN AT NIGHT.

BUT WHAT PERCENTAGE OF UPLANDERS TRULY BELIEVE WE EXIST?

VERY SOON WILL THE PLANET OF *BAJOR* BE AN *EMPTY WASTE*... THEN *WE* WILL EMERGE AND POPULATE THE PLANET ANEW.

EVEN *YOU* WHO CAME SEARCHING FOR EVIDENCE OF US... FLED IN *FEAR* WHEN YOU FOUND US, BUT THE TIME IS COME FOR OUR *EMERGENCE.*

OUR *DESTINY* IS TO PRESERVE THE RACE. ARE WE NOT THE *COUNCIL OF GUARDIANS?*

WE ARE THE HISTORY... AND THE FUTURE.

HERE. OPS. AUXILIARY POWER AUGMENTED. SEEMS WE HAD A BREAK IN THE PRIMARY POWER ON THE UPPER LEVELS. WE ARE INVESTIGATING.

KIRA TO OPS. REGARDING OUR CURRENT STATE OF AFFAIRS...

...I WOULD SUSPECT SOMETHING OTHER THAN A ROUTINE MALFUNCTION. TREAT THIS AS A POSSIBLE DANGEROUS SITUATION.

REPAIR TEAM ENROUTE WITH TWO FROM SECURITY. OPS OUT.

DAMN, I COULD USE ABOUT EIGHT MORE HANDS.

WOULD YOU LIKE TO BRING DORIEN UP FROM ENGINEERING?

NO, HE'S NEEDED THERE. I'LL MANAGE.

OH, NO...

LIEUTENANT?

THE DESTRUCTION OF BAJOR... IS NO MYTH.

CHECK MONITOR THREE... THEN CHECK MY NUMBERS ON THE TRAJECTORY.

CHIEF, STATUS REPORT ON THAT *PRIMARY* MALFUNCTION.

I THINK YOU'D BETTER CHECK *THIS* OUT *FIRST,* COMMANDER.

DAX?

FOR SEVERAL DAYS I HAVE BEEN TRACKING A *COMET.* THE COMET'S TRAJECTORY HAS JUST *CHANGED...* AND IT APPEARS TO BE ON A *COLLISION COURSE* WITH THE *WORMHOLE.*

THE COMET IS EXPELLING A DANGEROUS AMOUNT OF *RADIATION...*

EVEN IF THE COMET *MISSES* THE HOLE... RADIATION LEVELS, COMBINED WITH THE *PRE-EXISTING* RADIATION OF THE HOLE ITSELF, COULD LEAVE A CONTAMINATED FIELD IN PLACE FOR SEVERAL HUNDRED YEARS.

HOWEVER, I AM UNSURE ABOUT THE STORIES OF *EX-PLODING* HEAVENS, AND THE EFFECT ON THE PLANET *BAJOR.* I NEED FURTHER DATA ON THE COMET.

I WOULDN'T THINK A *COMET,* EVEN THAT *SIZE,* COULD HAVE A DAMAGING EFFECT ON THE *WORMHOLE.*

THE MESSENGER RETURNS.

OPS TO ODO.

ODO.

YOUR SECURITY TEAM HAS JUST DISCOVERED THE *SOURCE OF THE POWER FAILURE.* YOUR ASSISTANCE IS REQUIRED ON *LEVEL FIVE.*

THIS IS BECOMING TIRESOME.

Oh, YOU *LOVE YOUR JOB.*

HARDLY.

IT'S SO HARD TO TELL WHEN A SHAPESHIFTER IS ENJOYING HIMSELF.

IT'S HARD TO BELIEVE A RATIONAL PEOPLE COULD BE INCITED TO *VIOLENCE,* WHEN COOPERATION IS WHAT IS MOST NEEDED FOR THEIR OWN SURVIVAL.

THE *BAJORAN EMISSARIES* HAVE PUT IN AT DOCKING BAY FOUR.

I *STILL* DON'T UNDERSTAND WHY THEY INSIST ON A PERSONAL VISIT. ESPECIALLY NOW... IF THEY HAVE A *PROBLEM* WITH *OUR* HANDLING OF THE SITUATION, THERE ARE MORE PROPER CHANNELS...

YES, SIR, OVER HERE.

HE SEEMS TO HAVE BEEN *HOIST* WITH HIS OWN *PETARD*, AS IT WERE...

...CAUGHT IN HIS OWN BLAST.

MEANWHILE...

WE ARE FROM THE *BAJORAN COUNCIL OF GUARDIANS.* YOUR *BAJORAN* WILL KNOW US AS *THEY WHO WAIT.*

I...HAVE HEARD OF YOU, SIR.

THIS IS NOT A *SOCIAL* EXPEDITION. WE WISH TO CONFER WITH THE *COMMANDER* OF THIS STATION, PRIVATELY.

I AM COMMANDER SISKO. THESE ARE MY *CHIEF* OFFICERS, MAJOR KIRA AND LIEUTENANT DAX. PLEASE FOLLOW US AND WE WILL CONFER IN MY OFFICE.

PEKLAR AND SHIEV WILL ACCOMPANY US. TAKRA, YOU AND THE OTHERS WILL REMAIN.

YOU THINK *WE* ARE MERELY RELIGIOUS *ZEALOTS*, BENT ON SOME TRADITIONAL *REENACTMENT*. WE ARE MUCH MORE...

THIS IS NOT SOME GOD COME TO VISIT. THIS IS A *COMET* WE ARE TALKING ABOUT!

WE HAVE EXISTED APART FROM THE NATURAL WORLD FOR *TWO THOUSAND* YEARS, BUT WITH A SINGULAR PURPOSE...

TO FULFILL OUR *DESTINY*. THIS *MESSENGER*... IS OUR DESTINY!

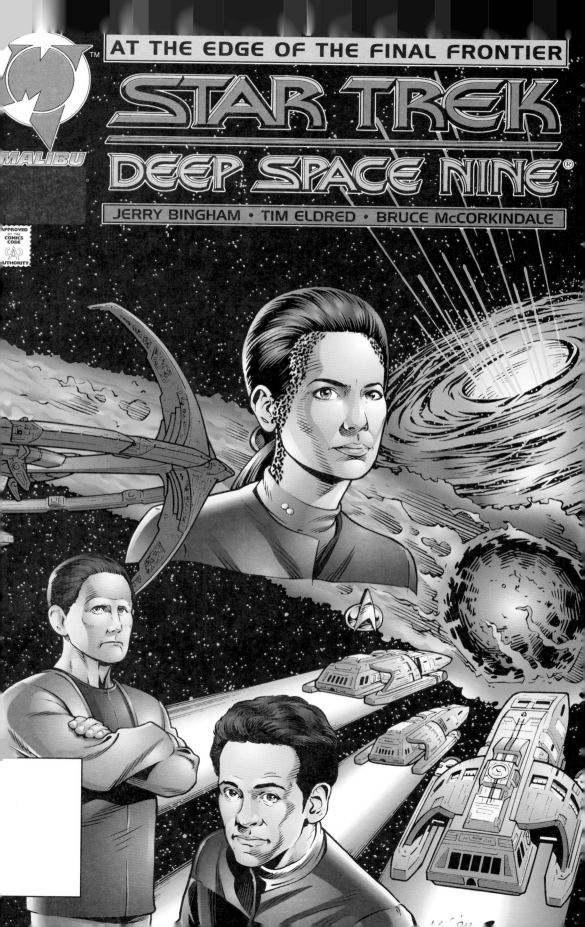

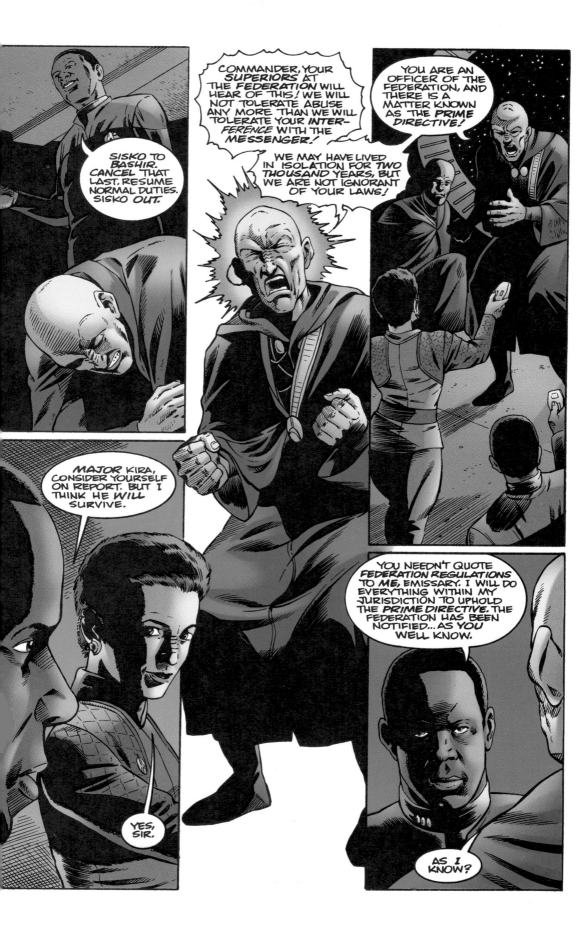

TEAM THREE TO OPS-- WE HAVE A *STAND-OFF*, MAIN CORRIDOR, LEVEL NINE. REQUEST *BACKUP!*

"OPS TO TEAM THREE. ALL SECURITY TEAMS ENGAGED...

"..HOLD POSITION."

ARGGH!

UNG!

AAAGT!

KIRBY...STAY WITH US! STAY WITH US!

SECURITY TEAM THREE-- MAN DOWN!

NEED EMERGENCY TELEPORT TO--

--THE INFIRMARY...

STATUS REPORT.

S-SORRY, SIR. WE HAVE THEM PINNED.

PHASERS?

ON HEAVY STUN, SIR, OF COURSE.

I WISH I COULD SAY THE SAME FOR THE OPPOSITION.

...I'M GOING TO HAVE A LITTLE DISCUSSION WITH OUR NEIGHBORS.

I SEE.

HOLD YOUR FIRE, UNLESS ATTACKED...

YES... S-SIR?

SIR, THEY SEEM TO BE USING A HEAVY STUN. CASUALTIES WILL RECOVER.

THEY ARE FOOLS. OURS IS A CAUSE WORTH DYING... AND KILLING FOR. THEY HAVE YET TO REALIZE THE SERIOUSNESS OF OUR MISSION.

COMMANDER SISKO?

YES, NOG?

I'M SCARED.

WE ALL ARE, SON. BUT WE FIGHT, AND *NEVER* SURRENDER TO OUR FEARS.

NOW LOCK THE DOORS AND BREAK OUT A HOLO-CHESS GAME. I'LL KEEP YOU INFORMED.

COMMANDER.

MAJOR.

I TAKE IT OUR GUESTS ARE SETTLED IN QUIETLY?

LET'S JUST SAY THEY'RE *SETTLED IN.* THEY HAD MUCH TO SAY ABOUT IT, HOWEVER.

I CAN IMAGINE.

Ah, *FINALLY.*

OPS TO SISKO. POWER RESTORED.

I SEE, CHIEF. *GOOD WORK.* BE WITH YOU IN FIVE.

I'VE GOTTEN WORD FROM THE FEDERATION.

I TAKE IT THE *WORD* WASN'T GOOD.

LESS THAN TWENTY HOURS, COMMANDER. AT THIS DISTANCE, I'VE BEEN ABLE TO MAKE A THOROUGH EXAMINATION OF THE COMET.

WE KNOW IT HAS A HYDROGEN CORONA LARGER THAN THAT OF A SMALL SUN. HOWEVER, AN EXAMINATION OF THE INTERIOR SHOWS ELE- MENTS OF A HEAVY HYDROGEN... A RADIO- ACTIVE ISOTOPE... FORMERLY KNOWN ONLY IN THE LABORATORY.

IT VERY MUCH RESEMBLES TITRIUM.

TITRIUM? I'M NOT SURE...

EARTH HISTORY, MAJOR. IT'S REALLY NOT SOMETHING YOU WOULD HAVE STUDIED. ITS ERA WAS SHORT-LIVED.

Eh, CHIEF?

OPPENHEIMER.

ODO TO OPS.

YES, ODO?

IF YOU WOULD BE SO KIND AS TO OPEN THE DOOR...

THIS MIGHT NOT BE A GOOD IDEA.

KLIK

COMMANDER?

ODO, YOU ARE THE MAN OF THE HOUR.

IF YOU DRANK, I'D BUY YOU AN OLD-FASHIONED *LAGER*.

WITH ME, ODO. IT'S TIME TO BECOME A *HERO*.

I THOUGHT I ALREADY WAS.

LET US KNOW WHEN YOU'VE LAUNCHED.

AYE, SIR.

SECURITY SEVEN TO OPS--DETENTION SUITE TWELVE VACATED! ONE UNIT DOWN!

DAMN THEM!

GOOD LUCK.

DON'T WOR ABOUT M CONCENTRA ON WHAT YO HAVE TO DO NOTHING MU INTERFER WITH THAT

I SEE YOURS IS A *TROUBLED* PEOPLE...LIVING BEHIND YOUR *MYTHOLOGIES.* YOU HAVE TAUGHT OTHERS TO *FEAR* YOU, BECAUSE YOU HAVE LIVED IN FEAR OF *DISCOVERY*... FOR TWO THOUSAND YEARS!

YOU CANNOT *BLIND* OTHERS TO THE *TRUTH!*.. THE *MESSENGER* IS OUR TRUTH -- OUR *WORD*, THE *WORD OF GODS!* YOU ARE NOT *BAJORAN* --

AND *YOU* ARE NOT BAJORAN!

LOOK AROUND ME...TRUE BAJORANS CAME OUT INTO THE *LIGHT, UNAFRAID!*

"THEIR WORLD WAS *CONSUMED*, YET THEY EMERGED AMID THE *WASTE*, AND THEY REBUILT THEIR *HOMES*, THEIR ENTIRE CIVILIZATION.

KIRA TO OPS. I'M IN.

"THEIRS WAS THE *TRUE COURAGE*. A PRIMITIVE PEOPLE, YET *UNAFRAID*.

...I'M IN.

"WHILE *YOU* HID BENEATH THE GROUND AND WROTE ON STONE YOUR *FEAR OF THE GODS*, THEY BUILT *SHIPS* AND SAILED TO THE *STARS*."

THIS IS NOT GOING TO WORK...

"WHILE *YOUR* DESTINY WAS DICTATED BY A PASSING *COMET*...THE *BAJORANS* WROTE, AND *CONTINUE* TO WRITE, THEIR *OWN*."

...I'VE LINKED MY *SCHEMATIC* TO EACH OF YOUR SECONDARY MONITORS.

MAJOR KIRA...*WORMHOLE* LATITUDE SIXTY-TWO POINT ONE SEVEN...

"...WE CAN ALLOW FOR A POINT TWENTY-FIVE *MARGIN OF ERROR*...WE HAVE APPROXIMATELY *NINETEEN* MINUTES..."

"*DR. BASHIR* -- *JULIAN* -- LONGITUDE THIRTY-ONE..."

NO! WE WILL NOT ALLOW A *HERETIC* TO TURN *US* FROM OUR PATH...

...TO TURN THE *MESSENGER* FROM ITS COURSE!

YOU MUST NOT ALLOW *HIM* TO INTERFERE!

"JULIAN, I NEED A MINOR COORDINATE CHANGE... POINT EIGHT FIVE DEGREES LONGITUDE..."

BLAST IT, I'M ONLY A *DOCTOR* WITH PILOT TRAINING!

YOU'RE DOING FINE, JULIAN. JUST MOVE TO STARBOARD. I'LL TELL YOU WHEN TO STOP.

I DO NOT WISH TO CHANGE YOUR DESTINIES... I WANT TO SAVE LIVES! HE CARES FOR NEITHER! WITH HIS WAY, THERE IS NO FUTURE... ONLY DEATH!

HE LIES TO TURN YOU FROM THE TRUTH! HE LIES!!

WE MAY DIE ANYWAY, BUT AT LEAST OUR FUTURE IS IN OUR HANDS!

GOOD, JULIAN. TWO MINUTES, SIX SECONDS. SHIELDS UP!

GRAPHIC NOVELS

ALIENS
☐ 0 7522 0878 0	Aliens v Preator – Deadliest of the Species 1	£9.99 pb
☐ 0 7522 0695 8	Aliens v Preator – Deadliest of the Species 2	£9.99 pb

RANMA
☐ 0 7522 0851 9	Ranma Book 1	£5.99 pb
☐ 0 7522 0861 6	Ranma Book 2	£5.99 pb

SPIDER-MAN
☐ 0 7522 0107 7	Masques	£8.99 pb
☐ 0 7522 0112 3	Perceptions	£8.99 pb
☐ 0 7522 0876 4	The Return of the Sinister 6	£9.99 pb
☐ 0 7522 0808 X	Revenge of the Sinister 6	£7.99 pb

STAR WARS
☐ 0 7522 0893 4	Classic – A New Hope	£8.99 pb
☐ 0 7522 0987 6	Dark Empire	£9.99 pb
☐ 0 7522 0822 5	Dark Empire 2	£9.99 pb
☐ 0 7522 0793 8	Dark Empire/Epilogue	£6.99 pb
☐ 0 7522 0616 8	Dark Lords of Sith 1	£8.99 pb
☐ 0 7522 0804 7	Droids	£8.99 pb
☐ 0 7522 0606 0	Empire Strikes Back	£7.99 pb
☐ 0 7522 0704 0	Jabba the Hutt	£8.99 pb
☐ 0 7522 0611 7	Return of the Jedi	£7.99 pb
☐ 0 7522 0798 9	River of Chaos	£8.99 pb
☐ 0 7522 0913 2	Star Wars Classic	£7.99 pb
☐ 0 7522 0747 4	Star Wars Classic 2	£9.99 pb
☐ 0 7522 0752 0	Star Wars Classic 3	£9.99 pb
☐ 0 7522 0817 9	Tales of the Jedi and Freedom Nadd Uprising	£10.99 pb

STAR TREK – DEEP SPACE NINE
☐ 0 7522 0928 0	Emancipation 1	£7.99 pb
☐ 0 7522 0933 7	Emancipation and Beyond	£7.99 pb
☐ 0 7522 0898 5	Hearts and Minds	£7.99 pb
☐ 0 7522 0888 8	Requiem	£7.99 pb

STREETFIGHTER
☐ 0 7522 0813 6	Street Fighter II – book 1	£6.99 pb
☐ 0 7522 0818 7	Street Fighter II – book 2	£6.99 pb

VARIOUS
☐ 0 7522 0897 7	Daredevil – man without fear	£9.99 pb
☐ 0 7522 0962 0	Necroscope	£7.99 pb
☐ 0 7522 0645 1	Marvels	£10.99 pb
☐ 0 7522 0881 0	Mask (film tie-in)	£6.99 pb
☐ 0 7522 0977 9	RoboCop: Prime Suspect	£7.99 pb
☐ 0 7522 0856 X	Shadow (film tie-in)	£6.99 pb
☐ 0 7522 0762 8	Species Movie (tie-in)	£8.99 pb

X MEN
☐ 0 7522 0892 6	Adventures	£9.99 pb
☐ 1 85283 390 4	Brood Trouble In The Big Easy	£5.25 pb
☐ 1 85283 394 7	Essential Guide	£9.99 pb
☐ 0 7522 0756 3	Gambit	£7.99 pb
☐ 0 7522 0691 5	Ghostrider/Wolverine/Punisher/Hearts of Darkness/Dark Design	£7.99 pb
☐ 0 7522 0871 3	God Loves, Man Kills	£5.99 pb
☐ 0 7522 0103 4	Rogue	£8.99 pb
☐ 0 7522 0803 9	Sabretooth	£6.99 pb
☐ 1 85283 395 5	Wolverine	£6.99 pb
☐ 0 7522 0108 5	Wolverine – Triumph and Tragedy	£9.99 pb
☐ 0 7522 0151 4	Uncanny X-Men: Acts of Vengeance	£8.99 pb
☐ 0 7522 0161 1	Uncanny X-Men: Wolverine/Psylocke 1	£8.99 pb

All these books are available at your local bookshop or can be ordered direct from the publisher. Just tick the titles you want and fill in the form below.

Prices and availability subject to change without notice.

Boxtree Cash Sales, P.O. Box 11, Falmouth, Cornwall TR10 9EN

Please send a cheque or postal order for the value of the book and add the following for postage and packing:

U.K. including B.F.P.O. – £1.00 for one book plus 50p for the second book, and 30p for each additional book ordered up to a £3.00 maximum.

Overseas including Eire – £2.00 for the first book plus £1.00 for the second book, and 50p for each additional book ordered.

OR please debit this amount from my Access/Visa Card (delete as appropriate).

Card Number ☐☐☐☐☐☐☐☐☐☐☐☐☐☐☐☐☐☐

Amount £ ....

Expiry Date ....

Signed ....

Name ....

Address ....